# ON CUE

Reg Smythe

RAVETTE BOOKS

© 1993 Mirror Group Newspapers, Ltd
Distributed by Syndication International
and North America Syndicate, Inc.

This edition first published by Ravette Books Limited 1993

This book is sold subject to the condition that it shall not, by way
of trade or otherwise, be lent, re-sold, hired out or otherwise
circulated without the publisher's prior consent in any form of
binding or cover other than that in which this is published and
without a similar condition including this condition being imposed
on the subsequent purchaser.

Printed and bound
for Ravette Books Limited
Egmont House, 8 Clifford Street,
London W1X 1RB
An Egmont Company
by Stige Arti Grafiche, Italy

ISBN: 1 85304 567 5

© 1986 Daily Mirror Newspapers, Ltd.
Dist. by News America Syndicate

CLUMP
CLUMP
CLUMP

THE WORST THING ABOUT
CREEPING INFLATION IS
HER GALLOPING REACTION

CAN I BUY YOU A DRINK, DEAR?

NO, THANKS, I'M OKAY. BUT YOU CAN COME AND CHAT AND TELL ME WHAT YOU'VE BEEN UP TO LATELY

© 1987 Daily Mirror Newspapers. Ltd
Dist. by North America Syndicate. Inc.
All rights reserved

IT *COULD* BE PIGEONS – BUT ON THE OTHER HAND I GOT A DISTINCT WHIFF OF AFTER-SHAVE –!

12-27

Smythe

Dist. by North America Syndicate, Inc.
All rights reserved

WELL, FOR A START — MY MISSUS IS FLAMING MAD AT *BOTH* OF US —

1-16

YOU'VE GOT TO WATCH 'EM.
ONCE IS A FAVOUR — DO
IT TWICE AND IT'S
YOUR JOB FOR LIFE

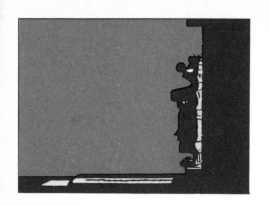

© 1991 M.G.N.
DIST. BY SYNDICATION INTERNATIONAL NORTH AMERICA SYNDICATE INC.

WHAT D'YOU MEAN BY COMING HOME AT FOUR IN THE MORNING?!!

© 1991 M.G.N.
DIST. BY SYNDICATION INTERNATIONAL NORTH
AMERICA SYNDICATE INC.

IN *HIS* CASE, IT ALWAYS DEPENDS ON HOW FAR AWAY THE LASS LIVES AND HOW MUCH BEFORE CLOSING TIME THE LAST BUS LEAVES

© 1991 M G N
DIST. BY SYNDICATION INTERNATIONAL NORTH
AMERICA SYNDICATE INC

...RIGHT, HERE GOES~!

HE'S HAD A FEW WHEN HE ACTS SO IMPULSIVELY AFTER ONLY STUDYING THE LASS FOR A COUPLE OF WEEKS

OH *NO!* IF IT ISN'T ONE THING IT'S ANOTHER —

© 1991 M.G.N.
DIST. BY SYNDICATION INTERNATIONAL NORTH AMERICA SYNDICATE INC.

A FINAL DEMAND! WE'VE GOT TO FIND SOME WAY OF PAYING THAT ELECTRIC BILL—

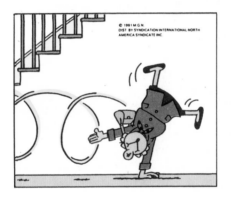

© 1991 M.G.N.
DIST. BY SYNDICATION INTERNATIONAL NORTH AMERICA SYNDICATE INC.

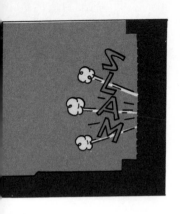

© 1991 M.G.N.
DIST. BY SYNDICATION INTERNATIONAL NORTH
AMERICA SYNDICATE INC.

© 1991 M.G.N.
DIST. BY SYNDICATION INTERNATIONAL NORTH
AMERICA SYNDICATE INC.

© 1985 M G N
DIST. BY SYNDICATION INTERNATIONAL NORTH
AMERICA SYNDICATE INC.

1-5

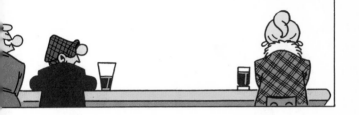

MINE NEVER GIVES OTHER WOMEN A SECOND LOOK — HE MAKES THE FIRST ONE A MARATHON

I'D CUT IT OUT, BUT I DON'T WANT HER TO LOSE HER ZEST FOR LIFE

1·26

©1992 M.G.H.
DIST. BY SYNDICATION INTERNATIONAL NORTH
AMERICA SYNDICATE INC.

©1992 M.G.N.
DIST. BY SYNDICATION INTERNATIONAL NORTH AMERICA SYNDICATE INC.

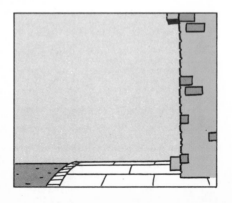

I DIDN'T LIKE THE LOOK ON HER CHOPS — I WOULDN'T PUT IT PAST HER TO MOVE SO I COULDN'T FIND HER WHEN I CAME BACK

©1992 M.G.N.
DIST. BY SYNDICATION INTERNATIONAL NORTH
AMERICA SYNDICATE INC.

SOME OF 'EM ARE PERFECTLY TRUE — !!

# ALSO IN THIS SERIES

# AFTER A FEW
# DON'T WAIT UP
# A BARREL OF LAUGHS

## £2.99
Available at your local bookshop or newsagent, or can be
ordered direct from the publisher. Just fill in the form below. Price
and availability subject to change without notice.

Ravette Books Limited, PO Box 11, Falmouth, Cornwall, TR10 9EN

Please send a cheque or postal order for the value of the book,
and add the following for postage and packing:
UK including BFPO — £1.00 per order.
OVERSEAS, including EIRE — £2.00 per order.
OR Please debit this amount from my Access/Visa Card (delete
as appropriate).

Card Number: [ ][ ][ ][ ][ ][ ][ ][ ][ ][ ][ ][ ][ ][ ][ ][ ][ ][ ]

EXPIRY DATE . . . . . . . . . . . . . .

SIGNED . . . . . . . . . . . . . . . . . . . . . . . . . . . . . . . . . . . . . .

NAME . . . . . . . . . . . . . . . . . . . . . . . . . . . . . . . . . . . . . . . .

ADDRESS . . . . . . . . . . . . . . . . . . . . . . . . . . . . . . . . . . . . .

. . . . . . . . . . . . . . . . . . . . . . . . . . . . . . . . . . . . . . . . . . . . . .